D0102945

DO SOMETHING ABOUT IT: **MAK** ~~APPLICATION~~

1. Using the analogy of a musical arrangement, describe what you have observed about the impact of your leadership upon the hearts of others. Is there discord? Is there harmony?

_____

_____

_____

_____

2. Consider your relationship with others. Using the chart below, how would you rate your relationships with those listed? Circle one for each relationship type.

Harmony or Discord Chart

Relationships with you and...	Harmony				Discord
1. God	1	2	3	4	5
2. Spouse	1	2	3	4	5
3. Children	1	2	3	4	5
4. Parents	1	2	3	4	5
5. Siblings	1	2	3	4	5
6. Friends	1	2	3	4	5
7. Neighbors	1	2	3	4	5
8. Boss	1	2	3	4	5
9. Co-workers	1	2	3	4	5
10. Your Own Personal Care	1	2	3	4	5

3. Describe how you believe God wants to use you as His
    instrument to create harmony and balance?

    _____

    _____

    _____

    _____

4. According to Dixon, Christ is the melody of the Christian
    leader's life to which every "instrument" of their lives must
    harmonize. What do you believe identifies your leadership as
    <u>Christian</u>? Explain why this is important.

    _____

    _____

    _____

    _____

5. Would those closest to you agree that your perception of your
    role as a leader is that of a servant? Explain.

    _____

    _____

    _____

    _____

6. Define servant leadership.

    _____

    _____

    _____

    _____

7. Citing Jesus' comments in Chapter One regarding the harvest,
    what can you learn from His example?
    a. The importance of praying for more laborers
    b. Choosing not to do everything, even when you can
    c. Being an example of not doing everything
    d. All of the above

8. As you consider Christ's example in this area, how does your leadership respond to overwhelming need?

_____
_____
_____
_____

9. In what ways do you allow others to *walk with* you?

_____
_____
_____
_____

10. If someone spent a typical day with you as you lead, what kinds of things would they learn?

_____
_____
_____
_____

BALANCE IN MARRIAGE

1. If those who "follow" you were rating who/what is first in your life based on their observations, who/what would they say comes before your mate? If you don't know, ask.

_____
_____
_____
_____

2. What is your mate's most frequent complaint?

_____
_____
_____
_____

3. How have you responded to that complaint thus far?

_____

_____

_____

_____

4. Consider Dixon's view that your mate sees things you cannot and vice versa. Examine the diagram below. Think of a time when you and your mate saw something differently. Write down your point of view on one side of the diagram and write down your mate's point on the other side of the diagram.

Range of vision both eyes can see

Range of vision only
one eye can see

Range of vision only
one eye can see

© 2004 Christina Dixon

What do you see?	What does your mate see?
_____	_____
_____	_____
_____	_____
_____	_____
_____	_____

5. Review your answers from the above chart. How often would you say you have discounted valuable information given to you by your mate? Explain.

_____

_____

_____

_____

6. How many hours do you tend to work per week?

_____

_____

_____

_____

7. What things do you do to assure your spouse of your love?

_____

_____

_____

_____

8. What additional things would you do if you had time?

_____

_____

_____

_____

BALANCE IN PARENTING

As generations before them, today's children are in desperate need of balanced examples of leadership. Remember, your responses during times of crisis are also examples of Christian leadership before the children you encounter.

If you are a leader with children, please answer the following questions from your experiences with your own children.

If you are a leader who does not have children, please answer the following questions from your experiences with the children of those you lead.

1. According to Dixon, what do leaders with children have the responsibility to prepare their children for?
   a. Knowing Who God is
   b. Life on their own
   c. Fulfilling the purpose for which God created them
   d. All of the above

2. Think about the last month. List the things you have done
    with your children to prepare them.

    _____   _____
    _____   _____
    _____   _____

3. Based on the things you have done with your children over the
    last two months, what would your children say you've done
    specifically with/for them to train them?

    _____   _____
    _____   _____
    _____   _____
    _____   _____

4. What two things does Dixon cite that leaders are very
    protective of that may hinder them from responding with
    balance when their children make mistakes?

    _____   _____

5. Have there been times when your child(ren)'s mistakes caused
    you to be concerned about your reputation? Explain.

    _____
    _____
    _____
    _____

BALANCE IN LEADING OTHERS

1. If someone spent a typical day with you as you lead, what
    kinds of things would they learn about balance? Explain.

    _____
    _____
    _____
    _____

2. Examine the marriages of those you lead. Take a week or two if necessary. How does your leadership contribute to their imbalance?

_____

_____

_____

_____

3. Too often there is an absence of balanced harmony in leadership due to a desire to _____

_____ .

4. What can pursuing a vision cause Christian leaders to do?

_____

_____

_____

_____

5. Read II Corinthians 10:8 and 13:10. What does Paul say is God's purpose for giving him authority?

_____

6. Explain the difference between service *for* God and responsibility *to* God.

_____

_____

_____

_____

7. How do the differences between the two impact Christian leaders' choices as they lead others?

_____

_____

_____

_____

Remember every leader can benefit from *balance.*

The purpose of the following questionnaire is to give you an opportunity to know how others perceive your leadership.

QUESTIONNAIRE	Rarely	Sometimes	Often
I am worried about my reputation.	☐	☐	☐
I value my spouse's opinion.	☐	☐	☐
Others seem to have difficulty approaching me.	☐	☐	☐
I tend to be impatient with people.	☐	☐	☐
I have difficulty delegating tasks.	☐	☐	☐
I *need* to oversee things.	☐	☐	☐
I can depend on those I delegate tasks to.	☐	☐	☐
Others are comfortable approaching me.	☐	☐	☐
I feel others take too long to get things done.	☐	☐	☐
I feel others aren't as concerned about the quality of the work as I am.	☐	☐	☐
I prefer to work alone. I don't like people *under* me.	☐	☐	☐
I have trouble when the attention isn't on me.	☐	☐	☐
I like being in control.	☐	☐	☐
My spouse understands when I don't treat him/her with kindness.	☐	☐	☐
Ministry gets the majority of my time.	☐	☐	☐
How things look is important to me.	☐	☐	☐

PRAY ABOUT IT: MAKE INTERCESSION

After completing the above chart download this page from the CD and give copies to others you know. Give them at least one week to answer these questions about you with no signatures, just check marks. To encourage honesty, you may consider giving them an anonymous way to return them.

Prayerfully review your answers as you compare them to the answers of others.

Write down the areas where you see consistencies.

_____   _____
_____   _____
_____   _____
_____   _____
_____   _____
_____   _____
_____   _____

Write down your prayer after examining which areas you've listed.

MEDITATE UPON IT: CONTEMPLATION

Consider the people that you are in relationship with as a leader or follower. Then think about your responses to this chapter, *"Balancing Your Mind and Your Ministry."* Now fill in the chart below:

HELP	I need to receive from:	I need to give to:
Healing		
Encouraging		
Loving		
Perspective		

What is your action plan to receive what you need in each of the following areas?

Healing -
Encouraging -
Loving -
Perspective -

What is your action plan to give what is needed in each of the following areas?

Healing -
Encouraging -
Loving -
Perspective -

Every leader can benefit from:

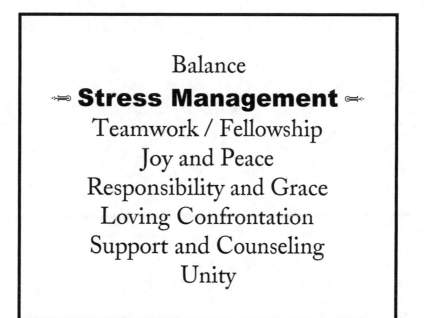

Balance
Stress Management
Teamwork / Fellowship
Joy and Peace
Responsibility and Grace
Loving Confrontation
Support and Counseling
Unity

~ Chapter 2 ~
Practical Stress Management for Leaders
Sabrina D. Black

THINK ABOUT IT:	GET REVELATION

SECTION I – INTRODUCTION

1. When you hear the words "Too blessed to be stressed or depressed" what comes to mind? What does this phrase mean to you?

_____

_____

_____

_____

2. Yes, we are blessed. Yet the reality of life for most Christians are breathless lives lived in the margins. What are some of the MARGINS that you have created in your life?

_____

_____

_____

_____

3. We overload ourselves. We are indeed "**too**." We are a society driven by extremes, pushing ourselves beyond the limits, constantly doing more and more. Have you ever been guilty of doing TOO?   ❏ Yes   ❏ No   ❏ Not Sure

4. According to Black, in Chapter Two, the overloaded lifestyles we live are detrimental to our p_____, e_____, s_____, and r_____ well-being.

5. We can lead a more stress-free life if we follow a few practical steps:

   a. Not only do we deal with external stressors but _____ as well, stress from our body and our _____.

   b. List some of the EXTERNAL stresses in your life:

       _____
       _____
       _____
       _____

   c. List some of the INTERNAL stresses in your life:

       _____
       _____
       _____
       _____

I urge you to be equipped, empowered, and encouraged to fulfill your calling. Providing hope, help, and healing to God's people requires leaders who have mastered the art of stress management. God wants leaders who know how to prevent stress and who know that there are provisions for us in the Bible when we are stressed.

6. What are some verses in the Bible that help you cope with and/ or avoid stress?

Verse A

_____

Verse B

_____

Verse C

_____

Stress, burnout, and compassion fatigue are occupational hazards that most pastors, leaders, and professional helpers encounter. The Lord extends this invitation in Matthew 11:28 to all those who are too blessed to be stressed or depressed, "Come unto me, all ye that labour and are heavy laden, and I will give you rest."

DO SOMETHING ABOUT IT: MAKE APPLICATION

SECTION II - TOO BLESSED

O, the joy of being in ministry, advancing the kingdom; making an impact in the earth locally and globally.

1. Identify one of your greatest joys regarding being in the ministry.

_____

_____

_____

2. Name one way in which you have made a local or global impact.

_____

_____

_____

God opens the windows of heaven and opportunities abound. There is so much to do and seemingly so little time.

3. What are ALL the things you are currently doing? Don't leave anything out. **List all of your roles and responsibilities:** (codes will be discussed later)

Roles and Responsibilities	CODE (AT, AP, AG)

The work is plentiful and the faithful laborers are few; so we must be about our Father's business, praying that He will raise up more faithful laborers for the harvest (Matthew 9:37-38).

4. Who are the people that you need more help from and in what areas?

Persons Name	Identify the area where you need help.

SECTION III - TO BE STRESSED OR DEPRESSED

What Is Stress? Review the chapter and the many ways that Black has defined stress.

1. STRESS can be defined as a number of normal reactions in the body (physical, emotional, mental, and spiritual) designed for

   _____.

2. STRESS is awareness that _____ and
   _____ are being disrupted.

3. STRESS lets us know that something is

   _____.

4. STRESS is an indication that something needs to change (usually our attitude, approach, or agenda) in order to maintain our _____ and a homeostatic state.

5. Look at your previous list of roles and responsibilities. Now ask yourself what needs to change: Your Attitude (AT), Approach (AP), or Agenda (AG)? Write next to each item listed one of the codes AT, AP, or AG.

What makes stress unpleasant and harmful is the feeling that we cannot escape it or the mindset that we are in bondage to it. Many of us need to change our mindset. The daily renewing of the mind; having the mind of Christ and knowing the heart of God can reduce stress.

6. We are not in bondage; we always have _____.

7. Look again at your list of roles and responsibilities. Identify a choice that you can make that relates to at least four of the different items listed.

#	Roles and Responsibilities	Choice
1		
2		
3		
4		

Let's pause. Take a few minutes to relax and **MEDITATE** on the Word. Don't study, just drink deeply of the assurance from II Corinthians 4:8-9, "We are troubled on every side, yet not distressed; we are perplexed, but not in despair; persecuted, but not forsaken; cast down, but not destroyed."

Be refreshed as you take time to savor the Scriptures below; they will encourage you as you seek to find balance in your leadership. Read the Scripture aloud and mediate on the portion of Scripture that is underlined and in bold:

2 Corinthians 12:10
So for the sake of Christ, I am well pleased and take pleasure in infirmities, insults, hardships, persecutions, perplexities and distresses; for when I am weak [in human strength], then am I [truly] strong (able, powerful in divine strength). AMP (*Meditate*)

Psalm 107:13-15
Then they cried to the Lord in their trouble, and **He saved them out of their distresses**. He brought them out of darkness and the shadow of death and broke apart the bonds that held them. Oh, that men would praise [and confess to] the Lord for His goodness and loving-kindness and His wonderful works to the children of men! AMP (*Meditate*)

Psalm 18:6
In my distress I called to the LORD; I cried to my God for help. From his temple **he heard my voice**; my cry came before him, into his ears. NIV (*Meditate*)

Psalms 4:1
To the Chief Musician; on stringed instruments. A Psalm of David.
ANSWER ME when I call, O God of my righteousness
(uprightness, justice, and right standing with You)! **You have
freed me when I was hemmed in and enlarged me when I was
in distress**; have mercy upon me and hear my prayer. AMP
(Meditate)

Romans 8:35-37
Who shall separate us from the love of Christ? Shall trouble or
hardship or persecution or famine or nakedness or danger or
sword? As it is written: "For your sake we face death all day
long; we are considered as sheep to be slaughtered." No, in all
these things **we are more than conquerors through him who
loved us.** NIV *(Meditate)*

SECTION IV – HOW STRETCHED AND STRESSED
AND ARE YOU?

   When conducting workshops on Stress Management there is an
object lesson that I like to use that you can participate in even now.
Pick up a rubber band and stretch it as far as you can. Now stretch
the rubber band again and again each time you think of all the
many roles and responsibilities you have. At some point people
will begin to frown and make faces while stretching the rubber
band. But I encourage them to keep stretching. Many will
respond "but it will break," "I don't want it to pop." "It might hurt
me or someone else if it snaps." And they are absolutely right. Yet
we rarely consider that we are stretching ourselves far beyond our
capacity to function at optimal levels. And we may soon reach our
breaking point, snap, and hurt someone.
   You may really need a break (stress relief) before you have a
breakdown. Many Christians have found themselves at the
breaking point at some time in their ministry. This need for stress
relief often becomes the justification for choices that are made in
an altered state of mind. When we are stressed, we function on
self-preservation. We operate in survival mode: How will I ever

get all of this done? Why do I have to do everything? How can I make it through this? When we are stressed, we stop looking up at God, or out to others but look primarily at ourselves.

Stress may be a WARNING SIGN that we need to examine our myths and/or our motives. When you begin to feel tense and overwhelmed, stop what you're doing and try to look at your situation from a fresh perspective.

Think about a current stressful situation and ask yourself the following questions:

1. "Why am I feeling this way?

_____

_____

_____

_____

2. "If this task doesn't get done, what's the worst thing that can happen?"

_____

_____

_____

_____

3. What is the absolute minimum that I need to do to complete this task? Be realistic.

_____

_____

_____

_____

4. Every assignment does not have to be perfect. If your assignment isn't perfect, is it really the end of the world?
   ❑ Yes   ❑ No

5. A year from now, will it be important?   ❑ Yes   ❑ No

When we are striving for excellence, we are doing the best that we can do without stretching ourselves to the limit and popping like the rubber band.

Too often we get stressed over everyday inconsequential things. Try to look at the "big picture." Think again about the above situation.

6. Who said you have to do it?

   _____

7. Can it be delegated to someone else?
   ❏ Yes   ❏ No

8. Is your way the only way to do what needs to be done?
   ❏ Yes   ❏ No

9. What are you trying to prove through completion of this task?

   _____
   _____
   _____
   _____

10. Who are you trying to prove it to?

    _____

We have too many Lone Rangers in ministry trying to do things themselves. So many of our leaders wear an "S" on their chest. However, it does not stand for "super," it stands for stretched to the point of "stressed."

We will need to let go of the myths surrounding the three areas (boundaries, perfectionism, and super syndrome) that often entrap spiritual leaders.

In the space provided write your answers to the following questions:

11. What has God called you to do?

    _____
    _____
    _____

12. What is your purpose?

_____

_____

_____

_____

13. What is your destiny?

_____

_____

_____

_____

14. What is your charge to fulfill?

_____

_____

_____

_____

15. Are you carrying out your responsibility and the responsibilities of others? Explain.

_____

_____

_____

_____

You may have twenty great projects but they may not all be for you to do (even if you have an administrator). We can avoid stress by serving in the areas where God has called us versus doing what everyone else wants us to do, or doing what is popular to be involved with at the time. We can reduce stress by not comparing our ministry with that of others. Nor should we try to keep up with where our friends and colleagues are serving.

Close your eyes for a moment and picture the area in which you work. Wow! Answer the following questions about your work space:

16. Is it cluttered or clear?

_____

_____

_____

_____

17. Can you actually put your hands on the tools and resources you need to be productive?

_____

_____

_____

_____

18. Is it a noisy or quiet place?

_____

_____

_____

_____

19. What are the sounds that you hear?

_____

_____

_____

_____

20. An effective way to reduce stress for some leaders is to modify or completely change their work environment. What are the things that you can change in your environment that will help you to be more productive?

_____

_____

_____

_____

Your level of fitness also impacts your perception, and your fitness influences your spiritual, behavioral, and emotional ability to deal with stressful circumstances. Total body fitness is crucial for effectively dealing with stressful situations.

As you answer these few questions you will be able find out how fit you are:

21. How many hours of sleep do you get each night? _____

22. Do you eat regular balanced meals each day?
    ❏ Yes   ❏ No   ❏ Sometime

23. Do you have a regular exercise program?
    ❏ Yes   ❏ No   ❏ Sometime

24. Do you spend time in quiet meditation?
    ❏ Yes   ❏ No   ❏ Sometime

25. Do you make time to enjoy fun and fellowship?
    ❏ Yes   ❏ No   ❏ Sometime

26. Information Over load

    a. What did people rely on in the past for their information?
        _____ of _____.

    b. According to Black, we have so much information but very little _____ or revelation.

27. False expectations

    c. Effective goals must be _____.

    d. Effective project planning includes at least these three elements: w_____ will do w_____ by w_____.

28. Social Isolation

Even though we can communicate with any one in the world, we often have little time to spend with people. Identify an impact of social isolation.

  a. The burden of possession

  b. Have you learned to "therewith be content"? Give an example. _____

  c. What were your last three purchases?

  _____

  _____

  _____

  d. Identify 10 things that you own (clothing, equipment, recreational items, books, tapes, etc) which you would be willing to give away that could be a blessing to someone else.

  _____   _____
  _____   _____
  _____   _____
  _____   _____
  _____   _____

30. The shrinking of time

We seem to have more to do in less time because we overcrowd our lives. Try the following three experiments over the next week.

  a. Take your watch off and listen to your internal clock. If you really need to know the time, ask someone. (Even if you are in an appointment; ask the other person to be aware of the time spent.)

  b. Take two things off your "to do list" each day and plan to sit still and meditate on the word of God.

c. Contact three people that are working with you or for you on various projects and give them more time to complete the assignment. (Depending on the project flow the time increments may be an additional two hours, two days or two weeks.)

31. Change
Change is one of the few things of which we can be certain.

a. In what ways have you changed in the past 6 months?

_____

_____

_____

_____

b. In what ways has your environment changed in the past 6 months?

_____

_____

_____

_____

c. In what ways have your commitments, roles, responsibilities, etc. changed in the past 6 months?

_____

_____

_____

_____

d. Have you embraced the above changes or are you struggling? What is necessary to help you adjust to the changes you have mentioned?

_____

_____

_____

_____

SECTION V – RECOGNIZING THE SIGNS AND EFFECTS OF STRESS

You know when you're stressed, right? Sometimes we don't, although the signs may be clear to others around us. Just remember that the signs are more pervasive than you think! Usually when we think of stress symptoms, we think of high blood pressure, elevated heart rate, overeating, and sweating too much. Signs of stress also include irritability, insomnia, anxiety, headaches, indigestion, muscle tension, jitteriness, and much more. Signs of stress fall into three categories: physical, emotional, and spiritual. Review the items listed in chart # 1 and identify the ways in which stress may be affecting you and the leaders around you. Circle each of the responses that you have experienced in the past thirty days. You may wish to ask someone who works closely with you to also complete the assessment regarding what they have observed through their interaction with you.

CHART #1 – Signs of Stress

PHYSICAL	EMOTIONAL	SPIRITUAL
Fatigue	Depression	Compromise
Sleeping	Anger	Loss of faith
Edginess	Defensiveness	Joyless
Indigestion	Nervous	Guilt/condemnation
Grooming	Anxiety	Blame-shifting
Body pain	Cynicism/sarcasm	Hopelessness

SECTION VI - TOO OVERWHELMED

As you read through this section, think about your own life and the lives of the people around you that impact you.

1. Busy-ness.

Being busy has become a way of life. I have learned to keep things moving. Christians are certainly not immune to busy-ness, as they try to fit church commitments, Bible study, and prayer into their already busy lives of work and family responsibilities. Now, picture the life of the leader of all these activities. It's tiring just thinking about it. Most leaders realize that they are "too busy", but deciding what activity to cut back is not easy.

A. List your top three areas of focus:

1. _____
2. _____
3. _____

Have your family or friends ever felt that your priorities were not balanced? Or that your "service to the ministry" was destroying your household?

B. What two or three activities did they think you were spending too much time on?

1. _____
2. _____
3. _____

C. What did they want you to spend the time doing instead?

_____
_____
_____
_____

2. *Technological speed.* Modern conveniences have increased our sense of urgency. We want everything done right away. If our activities were limited to those we could carry out without technology most of us would have much quieter lives. Telephones, fax machines, computers and email add to the speed of life.

A. When was the last time you sent a hand-written correspondence? _____

Take time this week and write (a letter, postcard, or greeting card) to five people you have not spoken with in the past 30 days.
List the names of the people you are considering:

1. _____
2. _____
3. _____
4. _____
5. _____

B. How often do you check your email? _____

C. When you are at the computer, do you find that you do other
things as well? _____

D. How much time do you spend on the computer?

_____

E. How much time do you spend in each category daily?

_____ surfing the internet _____ playing games _____ chat rooms

_____ email _____ typing _____ other

SECTION VII – TOO OVERLOADED

As you read the Overloaded checklist, mark the ones that apply to
you. You may even wish to list specific items in each area on the
line provided. This may take some time to do. Don't stress. Give
careful consideration to each area so that you can make the
necessary changes to alleviate some of the stress in your life.

Chart # 2 – Overloaded

Are You Overloaded?

_____ Activity Overload	_____
_____ Change Overload	_____
_____ Choice Overload	_____
_____ Commitment Overload	_____
_____ Competition Overload	_____
_____ Debt Overload	_____
_____ Decision Overload	_____
_____ Education Overload	_____
_____ Expectation Overload	_____
_____ Fatigue Overload	_____
_____ Hurry Overload	_____
_____ Information Overload	_____
_____ Media Overload	_____
_____ Ministry Overload	_____
_____ Noise Overload	_____
_____ People Overload	_____
_____ Pollution Overload	_____
_____ Possession Overload	_____
_____ Problem Overload	_____
_____ Technology Overload	_____
_____ Traffic Overload	_____
_____ Waste Overload	_____
_____ Work Overload	_____

If you are an overloaded leader, pause and thank God for the relief that He provides. Praise God for this book, for the upcoming conferences, and the authors who are available to minister to you at your point of need.

Leaders that are overloaded need to establish appropriate boundaries, set loving limits, learn to say NO (even to other leaders), and be realistic about what they are able to accomplish. This can be challenging, but remember we can't do everything and God only expects us to do those things He has called us to do. Leaders must learn to discern the voice of God. Has He really called you to be involved in every project that is on your agenda?

When you take on a new project you may need to let two to three other things go. Leaders must discern between better and best.

SECTION VIII – EQUIPPED, EMPOWERED, AND ENCOURAGED

When God calls you to leadership, He does indeed equip you for the work of the ministry and he raises up others around you to help bear the burden of leading the people.

Read the story Moses in Exodus 18.

1. What insights did you gain from that text?

_____

_____

_____

_____

2. List three things that you can apply to your life that will help reduce the stresses of leadership?

    a._____

    b. _____

    c._____

God also empowers you with wisdom and grace, with knowledge and balance. God encourages you and sends those with the gift of encouragement to help edify you and build you up. When we find ourselves stressed, it is an indication that we need to re-examine our focus, our purpose, and our destiny.

Here are some simple things you can do *today* to control, reduce, or prevent stress. This list of stress reducers is compiled from interviews with leaders and followers. Many of the ideas were repeated. As you read through the items listed in Chart #3, circle 5-7 items that you can implement today that will help you reduce your stress.

Practical Techniques for Rest Relaxation and Spiritual Renewal
CHART #3 – Stress Reduction / Simple Things you can do Today

• Simplify and unclutter your life.	• Spend time in prayer and meditation.
• Pamper yourself (rest, body massage, facial, manicure, make-over, etc.).	• Get away from your daily stresses with group sports, social events and hobbies.
• Obey God.	• Pray continually.
• Practice the presence of God.	• Listen to soft, soothing music.
• Exercise (run, walk, bike, swim, tennis, golf, garden, etc.).	• Just Say No. . . to projects that won't fit into your schedule.
• Fellowship with the body of Christ.	• Memorize and meditate on Scripture.
• Get organized so everything has its place.	• Keep a folder of favorite Scriptures on hand.
• Maintain accountability.	• Praise and worship.
• Have backups; an extra car key in your wallet, an extra house key buried in the garden, extra stamps, etc.	• When you are not able to K.I.S.S. (Keep It Sweet & Simple) then K.M.S. (Keep Mouth Shut.).
• Sit on your ego. It's about you but it's not about you.	• Do something for the Kid in You everyday.
• Go to bed on time.	• Get enough exercise.
• Get up on time so you can start the day.	• Carry a Bible with you to read while waiting in line.
• Encourage yourself with spiritual readings.	• Be kind to unkind people (they probably need it the most).
• Listen to songs of praise and worship.	• Give, share, or help someone else.
• Pace yourself. Spread out big changes and difficult projects over time; don't lump the hard things all together.	• Remember that the shortest bridge between despair and hope is often a good "Thank you Lord!"
• Delegate tasks to capable others.	• Laugh and Laugh some more!
• Allow extra time to do things and to get to places.	• Take your work seriously, but yourself not at all.

• Less is more. (Although one is often not enough, two are often too many).	• Develop a forgiving attitude (most people are doing the best they can).
• Pray.	• Eat right.
• Take one day at a time.	• Slow down.
• Learn the Serenity Prayer.	• Talk less; listen more.
• Live within your budget; don't use credit cards for ordinary purchases.	• Have fun and laugh out loud (a merry heart doeth good like medicine).
• Breathe slowly and deeply. Before reacting to the next stressful occurrence, take three deep breaths and release them slowly.	• Choose one simple thing you have been putting off (e.g. returning a phone call, making a doctor's appointment) and do it immediately.
• Listen to a tape while driving that can help improve your quality of life.	• Get outdoors for a brief break. There is healing power in the air.
• Write thoughts and inspirations down.	• Talk out loud to a friend/counselor.
• Plan something rewarding for the end of your stressful day, even if only a relaxing bath or half an hour with a good book.	• Do a quick posture check. Hold your head and shoulders upright and avoid stooping or slumping.
• Having problems? Talk to God and get counsel.	• Don't worry about things you can't control, like the weather.
• Make friends with Godly people.	• Sleep and periods of relaxation.
• Every night before bed, think of things you're grateful for.	• Don't be a procrastinator or perfectionist.
• Everyday, find time to be alone.	• Develop an action / contingency plan.
• Remind yourself that you are not the general manager of the universe.	• Identify the worse case scenario but trust the sovereignty of God.

It is important to remember your relationship with God. When you are stressed, you need to remember that you are not alone, and that God's love for you is constant. Use Scriptures to help you.

Psalms 121:1-2a "I will lift up mine eyes to the hills, from whence cometh my help. My help comes from the Lord."

Remember every leader can benefit from effective *stress management*.

PRAY ABOUT IT:	MAKE INTERCESSION

Take some time to write a prayer of praise and thanksgiving to God. Praise God for revealing your need for rest and relaxation. Rejoice and again I say rejoice.

MEDITATE UPON IT:	CONTEMPLATION

Consider the people that you are in relationship with as a leader or follower. Then think about your responses to this chapter, *"Stress Management."* Now fill in the chart below:

HELP	I need to receive from:	I need to give to:
Healing		
Encouraging		
Loving		
Perspective		

What is your action plan to receive what you need in each of the following areas?

Healing -
Encouraging -
Loving -
Perspective -

What is your action plan to give what is needed in each of the following areas?

Healing -
Encouraging -
Loving -
Perspective -

Every leader can benefit from:

Balance
Stress Management
⊶ **Teamwork / Fellowship** ⊷
Joy and Peace
Responsibility and Grace
Loving Confrontation
Support and Counseling
Unity

~ Chapter 3 ~
Leaving the Lone Ranger Mentality ~ Alone
Brenda A. Jenkins

THINK ABOUT IT: **GET REVELATION**

---

*People grow through experience if they meet life
honestly and courageously. – Eleanor Roosevelt*

<u>Introduction</u>

I have heard people say, "I do not need people, as long I have God, I am OK." Others may feel they are self-sufficient within themselves and in need of no one. The latter is what has been called the Lone Ranger Mentality. Neither perspective is in line with God's purpose for His creation.

1. When you come into difficult relationships in your daily life, do you examine yourself? ❑ Yes   ❑ No

2. Does what you are doing match God's standards of relating to His people? ❑ Yes   ❑ No

Being obedient to God's Word leads to fellowship with Him and others. We are all a part of a bigger purpose. God wants all of us to work together using our skills and gifts.

Being a Lone Ranger disconnects you from God's purpose for you, and it disconnects you from others. There is your way, the other person's way, and God's way.

3. Does your way match God's way? ❑ Yes   ❑ No

4. Does it glorify Him? ❑ Yes   ❑ No

5. Would you like to live your life for God in fellowship with Him and others? ❑ Yes   ❑ No

---

DO SOMETHING ABOUT IT: MAKE APPLICATION

Let's work through some of the exercises in this chapter to see if you can live a more victorious life.

Section 1 – Current Condition

1.   What conditions does Dr. Tony Evans say this world is in?

_____

_____

_____

_____

2. Think of the last time you had some type of conflict with another person in your life. Give an example where the other person wronged you. Write out what happened.

_____

_____

_____

_____

3. Examining the above, re-word what happened taking responsibility for your actions.

_____

_____

_____

_____

4. Explain possible ways you could help resolve the conflict using application of God's Word.

_____

_____

_____

_____

5. Refer to the text, then in your own words explain Dr. Michael A. Proud Jr.'s statement *"Living in a free society as we do, that concept of freedom and independence can evade every part of our lives, even our spiritual lives. It can create in our minds a lone-ranger mentality of life, that is, I don't need anyone and I can live as I like"* (Proud, 2002, para 8).

_____

_____

_____

_____

6. Refer to the text, then in your own words explain Dr. Michael A. Proud Jr's statement *"Yet, our love affair with independence can hinder our willingness to depend upon God and on others"* (Proud, 2002, para 8).

_____

_____

_____

_____

7. Define "Lone Ranger Mentality" and explain any areas of your life where you may be showing signs of this life style.

_____

_____

_____

_____

8. Define God's directive based on I John 4:7-8.

_____

_____

_____

_____

9. Define fellowship.

_____

_____

_____

_____

10. List ways you fellowship with God.

_____

_____

_____

_____

11. List people you are in fellowship with and their relationship with you.

_____

_____

_____

_____

12. In this chapter Jenkins talks about "A Path to Fellowship" explain.

_____

_____

_____

_____

13. What are two of the barriers mentioned in the chapter that prevent fellowship?

R_____

T_____

14. List the 5R's sorted by God versus Man.

R _____ vs R_____

R _____ vs R_____

R _____ vs R_____

R _____ vs R_____

R _____ vs R_____

15. Refer to the 5R's chart and discuss God's verses Man's responsibility as it relate to "Restoration".

_____

_____

_____

_____

16. Select one of the R's you would like to improve in your life. List what improvements you would like to implement.

_____

_____

_____

17. Research your Bible and list Scriptures that will help you with the area listed in the prior question. (With each Scripture, write an application to your life in your own words).

_____

_____

_____

_____

18. What are some of the things Jenkins lists that can cause trust to break down?

_____

_____

_____

_____

19. List those areas that cause trust to break down that someone has done to you.

_____

_____

_____

_____

20. Look up Scriptures (from Truth chart) that apply to those areas you listed above. Write out Scripture.

_____

_____

_____

_____

21. Refer to the Truth Scriptures chart; look up Scripture(s) that relate to an action in the "Your Actions" column. Write out each Scripture.

_____

_____

_____

_____

22. Meditate on Psalm 37. Write down how this helped you.

_____

_____

_____

_____

23. Discuss the two Biblical examples Paul used for forgiveness and reconciliation from the book.

_____

_____

_____

_____

24. Explain the suggestions Jenkins provided for those who are lonely. (Scenario 1)

_____

_____

_____

_____

25. What is the difference between being a loner and being lonely? (Scenario 1)

_____

_____

_____

_____

26. Explain the suggestions Jenkins provided for dealing with those who have loved ones going down the wrong road. (Scenario 2)

_____

_____

_____

_____

27. Describe how you can apply Jenkins' suggestion to someone you love. (Scenario 2)

_____
_____
_____
_____

28. Explain the suggestions Jenkins provide for dealing with someone who criticizes you. (Scenario 3)

_____
_____
_____
_____

29. Explain Eph. 4:22 – 24 and write down the application to a situation in your life.

_____
_____
_____
_____

30. Consider the refrigerator story, identify something God has told you to improve on or clean up and write down a plan to make improvements.

_____
_____
_____
_____

31. As explained by Jenkins in her summary what protects us when we experience pain?

_____
_____
_____
_____

32. List future areas you will work on after mastering these.

_____

_____

_____

_____

As part of your continuous improvements redo this chapter as needed.

Remember every leader can benefit from *teamwork and fellowship.*

PRAY ABOUT IT:	MAKE INTERCESSION

Let's pray. Take some time to communicate with God about your feelings. Ask for guidance for all that you do in Jesus' name. Write your personal prayer here.

MEDITATE UPON IT: CONTEMPLATION

Consider the people that you are in relationship with as a leader or
follower. Then think about your responses to this chapter,
"Leaving the Lone Ranger Mentality - Alone" Now fill in the chart
below:

HELP	I need to receive from:	I need to give to:
Healing		
Encouraging		
Loving		
Perspective		

What is your action plan to receive what you need in each of the
following areas?

Healing -
Encouraging -
Loving -
Perspective -

What is your action plan to give what is needed in each of the
following areas?

Healing -
Encouraging -
Loving -
Perspective -

Every leader can benefit from:

Balance
Stress Management
Teamwork / Fellowship
Joy and Peace
Responsibility and Grace
Loving Confrontation
Support and Counseling
Unity

~ Chapter 4 ~
Leadership in Crisis
Pamela J. Hudson

THINK ABOUT IT:	GET REVELATION

"Depression knows no boundaries. 1 out of 6 Americans adults
have depression during their life time."

1. Looking at the symptoms of depression listed in chapter four,
   discuss the definition of depression and the associated
   symptoms.

   _____

   _____

   _____

   _____

2. Do you recognize yourself in the symptoms listed?

   ❏ Yes   ❏ No

3. How many of the symptoms have (had) you experienced in the last year? _____

4. Which are you experiencing now?

_____

_____

_____

_____

5. Do you know any pastors, ministers, or laypersons who have experienced burnout? ❏ Yes   ❏ No

6. Which of the symptoms of depression did you notice in their lives?

_____

_____

_____

_____

7. Look at Psalm 42. What does the Bible say about depression?

_____

_____

_____

_____

8. What is God's answer to this disease?

_____

_____

_____

_____

DO SOMETHING ABOUT IT: MAKE APPLICATION

1. What causes church leadership to not seek help?

   _____

   _____

   _____

   _____

2. Has your pride, position, or intellect deceived you to not seek assistance when you were hurting? ❏ Yes   ❏ No

3. Name the last time you needed help but refused to get it. What was your reason?

   _____

   _____

   _____

   _____

4. When was the last time you were angry?

   _____

   _____

   _____

   _____

5. Are you angry with someone now? If you answered yes, identify with whom. ❏ Yes   ❏ No

   _____

6. How have you exercised restraint as noted in Proverbs 15:1 toward the person you are or were angry with?

   _____

   _____

   _____

   _____

7. In the past 18 months, when was the last time you forgave someone?

_____

8. Name the person (s).

_____

9. How has the act of forgiveness changed your life and or attitude?

_____

_____

_____

_____

10. Are you mentally or physical overwhelmed? ❏ Yes ❏ No

11. How has this affected how many hours of sleep you get weekly?

_____

_____

_____

_____

12. Explain the reason for your restless nights.

_____

_____

_____

_____

13. When was the date of your last physical examination?
Date_____

14. What were the results and your doctor's recommendations?

_____

_____

_____

_____

15. Read Psalm 4:8 and Proverbs 3:24. Explain how these verses can aid you to a peaceful rest.

_____

_____

_____

_____

16. What type of massive changes has your ministry undergone?

_____

_____

_____

_____

17. How have these changes impacted you?

_____

_____

_____

_____

18. Did you delegate responsibility or are you doing it all?
    ❑ Yes   ❑ No

19. How have the goals or expectations of ministry changes been defined or communicated clearly by you to your staff?

_____

_____

_____

_____

20. Write out your understanding of your role and responsibility as the leader.

_____

_____

_____

_____

21. What can you do to better articulate the vision for the ministry?

_____

_____

_____

_____

22. Explain the role the Holy Spirit has in your responsibility as leader.

_____

_____

_____

_____

23. What was the occasion the last time you asked for the Holy Spirit's help?

_____

_____

_____

_____

24. According to Hudson, how does God describe your role as leader?

_____

_____

_____

_____

25. Some core competencies mentioned by Hudson are: character, integrity, honesty, dignity, and planning. Discuss their importance in leadership, and then rate their importance on the chart below.

_____

_____

_____

_____

Core Competency	Rate Importance to Leadership from 1 to 5 1 = Unimportant 5 = Important				
Character	1	2	3	4	5
Integrity	1	2	3	4	5
Honesty	1	2	3	4	5
Dignity	1	2	3	4	5
Planning	1	2	3	4	5

_____

_____

_____

_____

26. Which of these attributes do you see in your leadership?

_____

_____

_____

_____

27. Rank yourself on a scale of 1-10 (10 being highest) in each of Hudson's core competencies.

Core Competency	Incompetent									Competent
Character	1	2	3	4	5	6	7	8	9	10
Integrity	1	2	3	4	5	6	7	8	9	10
Honesty	1	2	3	4	5	6	7	8	9	10
Dignity	1	2	3	4	5	6	7	8	9	10
Planning	1	2	3	4	5	6	7	8	9	10

28. Name some other core competencies.

_____

_____

_____

_____

29. How could you add these to your leading style?

_____

_____

_____

_____

Examine the following leadership traits and how each applies to you: Open Communication, Unity, Flexible toward Change, Respect for Authority, Reasoning and Zeal with Knowledge.

30. What is the state of your communication with God?

_____

_____

_____

_____

31. How effective are you in communicating goals and objectives to your staff?

 ❏ Highly effective
 ❏ Moderately Effective
 ❏ Somewhat Effective
 ❏ Improvement Needed

32. What could you do to improve communications with God and your staff?

_____

_____

_____

_____

33. How has your attitude as a leader compromised harmony in the church, office or the home?

_____

_____

_____

_____

34. According to Ephesians 4:3 what is needed to foster a sense of unity?

_____

_____

_____

_____

35. How determined are you in your mind to facilitate positive change?
 ❏ Highly Determined
 ❏ Moderately Determined
 ❏ Somewhat Determined
 ❏ Improvement Not Determined

36. Have you decided what changes you need to implement for the betterment of the organization? List five changes.

_____

_____

_____

_____

_____

37. How do you know you made significant strides toward your goals in your role as a leader?

_____

_____

_____

_____

38. What major or minor changes have you made in the last six months?

_____

_____

_____

_____

39. What affect did the changes have on you, your family, ministry, and/or staff?

_____

_____

_____

_____

40. Do your workers have a high regard for you as a person or leader? ❑ Yes   ❑ No   Explain.

_____

_____

_____

_____

41. How do you they demonstrate their respect for you?

_____

_____

_____

_____

42. How do you demonstrate your respect for your staff?

_____

_____

_____

_____

43. Will they agree that you respect them and the work they do?
    ❏ Yes   ❏ No   Explain.

_____

_____

_____

_____

44. Would God agree that in your responsibility as leader you have
    respect for His Word? ❏ Yes   ❏ No   How So?

_____

_____

_____

_____

45. Do you have a plan on how to carry out your task as leader?
    ❏ Yes   ❏ No

46. Write the vision or mission statement.

_____

_____

_____

_____

47. How committed are you to the vision God has for your life?

_____

_____

_____

_____

48. In the last five years, what have you done to empower yourself, educate yourself, and enrich your life to skillfully understand the Word of God?

_____

_____

_____

_____

49. If you could write a 50-word summation of how Nebuchadnezzar missed understanding his role as a leader, what would you write?

_____

_____

_____

_____

_____

_____

_____

50. How does Psalm 62:5 motivate you to become more God conscious?

_____

_____

_____

_____

51. What have you been saying/confessing about your ministry, staff, and family in the last 18 months?

_____

_____

_____

_____

52. What seeds of "hope, help, and healing" have you spoken into your ministry? Write them down.

_____

_____

_____

_____

53. If you have been speaking negatively about your role as leader, how would you go about changing the words that come out of your mouth? Explain.

_____

_____

_____

_____

54. Describe your prayer and praise life.

_____

_____

_____

_____

55. Take a look at the depression chart in chapter four. Describe the two parallels of how leaders should handle or respond to circumstances.

_____

_____

_____

_____

56. Which one describes how you handled that last crisis at home?

_____

_____

_____

_____

57. What about in the office with your staff?

_____

_____

_____

_____

58. Which side of the depression chart do you find yourself?
    Fear/Anger   Thanksgiving
    Self-Pity   Peace
    Depression
    Despair

59. When was the last time you were jealous of someone else and/or ministries?

_____

_____

_____

_____

60. Explain the role jealousy and rage have in the deterioration of leadership.

_____

_____

_____

_____

61. Describe how you dealt with a recent crisis that challenged your leadership.

_____

_____

_____

_____

62. What did you learn about yourself?

_____

_____

_____

_____

63. What area of your personality did you have to confront that was not Biblical or pleasing to God?

_____

_____

_____

_____

64. Describe how you identify with David, Saul, Nebuchadnezzar, or Elijah as leaders.

_____

_____

_____

_____

_____

_____

65. What characteristics of these men do you see in your life as a leader?

_____

_____

_____

_____

66. What lessons from their lives would you as a leader avoid?

_____

_____

_____

_____

Remember every leader can benefit from *joy and peace.*

| PRAY ABOUT IT: | **MAKE INTERCESSION** |

Write a prayer for someone who is a leader. Write a prayer for yourself.

MEDITATE UPON IT: CONTEMPLATION

Consider the people that you are in relationship with as a leader or follower. Then think about your responses to this chapter, *"Leadership in Crisis."* Now fill in the chart below:

HELP	I need to receive from:	I need to give to:
Healing		
Encouraging		
Loving		
Perspective		

What is your action plan to receive what you need in each of the following areas?

Healing -
Encouraging -
Loving -
Perspective -

What is your action plan to give what is needed in each of the following areas?

Healing -
Encouraging -
Loving -
Perspective -

Every leader can benefit from:

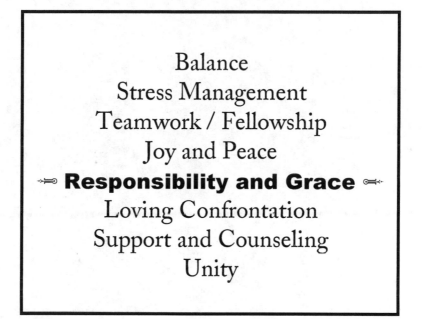

Balance
Stress Management
Teamwork / Fellowship
Joy and Peace
Responsibility and Grace
Loving Confrontation
Support and Counseling
Unity

~ Chapter 5 ~
Providing Counseling & Compassion to Christians Who Are Irresponsible
Christina Dixon

THINK ABOUT IT:	GET REVELATION

1. The harm experienced by families resulting from irresponsible behavior is e_____ and less v_____.

2. What perpetual state is caused by irresponsibility? _____

3. Write at least five examples that Dixon gives as irresponsible behavior?

   _____   _____
   _____   _____
   _____   _____
   _____   _____

4. Of those listed, in the book in Chapter 5, which examples
    seem more common in your leadership?

    _____

    _____

    _____

    _____

5. Of those listed which examples seem more common among
    those you lead?

    _____   _____

    _____   _____

    _____   _____

    _____   _____

6. Which of the following items eat away at personal productivity
    like parasites?
    a. Unresolved issues from childhood
    b. Lack of proper training
    c. Lack of understanding
    d. All of the above

7. What many call "not babying people," Dixon calls a…

    _____

8. Write down the definition of irresponsibility.

    _____

    _____

    _____

    _____

9. Read Galatians 6:4. Write down what this verse means in your own words.

_____

_____

_____

_____

10. How can applying this Scripture help those who are irresponsible?

_____

_____

_____

_____

DO SOMETHING ABOUT IT: MAKE APPLICATION

SELF-EVALUATION

1. When I am called upon to answer for my behavior, how do I tend to respond?

_____

_____

_____

_____

2. Am I willing to give an account as the primary cause, motive, or agent regarding matters of importance? Or do I pass the buck and cast blame? Explain.

_____

_____

_____

_____

3. Do people tend to find it difficult to believe things I tell them because I've shown myself to be untrustworthy? How does this relate to irresponsibility? Explain.

_____

_____

_____

_____

4. Do I consistently choose between right and wrong for myself? Or do I *need others* to keep me out of trouble and focused on the right things? How does this relate to being responsible? Explain.

_____

_____

_____

_____

5. Do others find me too immature to admit when I make mistakes? Explain.

_____

_____

_____

_____

6. When I "delegate" my responsibility to others, it is because...

_____

_____

_____

_____

7. In the areas where you are irresponsible, how would you want others to treat you?

_____

_____

_____

_____

8. What are some carnal responses to irresponsible people?
   a. Ignoring them
   b. Avoiding them
   c. Patronizing them
   d. Speaking the truth harshly
   e. All of the above

9. At times attempts to help irresponsible people end up causing them to feel _____ .

10. In the section entitled, Tomato Wisdom, what does Dixon say our lives and methods must be tied to? _____

11. Explain the difference between praying for people and praying about them.

_____

_____

_____

_____

12. As one created in God's image, each person has the right to choose their behavior.
    ❏ True   ❏ False   Explain.

_____

_____

_____

_____

13. It is possible to accept a person and reject their behavior.
    ❑ True   ❑ False   Explain.

_____

_____

_____

_____

14. Even though irresponsible people have done the same things
    for years, they can still change.
    ❑ True   ❑ False   Explain.

_____

_____

_____

_____

15. As a Christian leader, I am empowered to express kindness to
    others, including those who are irresponsible.
    ❑ True   ❑ False   Explain.

_____

_____

_____

_____

16. It may take a long time for irresponsible people to become
    accustomed to making responsible choices.
    ❑ True   ❑ False   Explain.

_____

_____

_____

_____

17. Irresponsible people may be God's way of giving others
    opportunity to develop patience.
    ❏ True   ❏ False   Explain.

    _____

    _____

    _____

    _____

18. Others, including you, may be contributing to the continuance
    of irresponsible behavior.
    ❏ True   ❏ False   Explain.

    _____

    _____

    _____

    _____

19. Resistance and resentment are often the irresponsible person's
    response to feeling controlled.
    ❏ True   ❏ False   Explain.

    _____

    _____

    _____

    _____

20. It is wrong to say "No" to an irresponsible person?
    ❏ True   ❏ False   Explain. Give scriptural basis.

    _____

    _____

    _____

    _____

Remember every leader can benefit from *responsibility and grace.*

PRAY ABOUT IT: MAKE INTERCESSION

1. Write down your prayer for the irresponsible things you've learned about yourself.

2. Write down your prayer for those in your life who exhibit irresponsible behavior.

MEDITATE UPON IT:	**CONTEMPLATION**

Consider the people that you are in relationship with as a leader or follower. Then think about your responses to this chapter, *"Providing Counseling & Compassion to Christians Who Are Irresponsible."* Now fill in the chart below:

HELP	I need to receive from:	I need to give to:
Healing		
Encouraging		
Loving		
Perspective		

What is your action plan to receive what you need in each of the following areas?

Healing -
Encouraging -
Loving -
Perspective -

What is your action plan to give what is needed in each of the following areas?

Healing -
Encouraging -
Loving -
Perspective -

Every leader can benefit from:

Balance
Stress Management
Teamwork / Fellowship
Joy and Peace
Responsibility and Grace
Loving Confrontation
Support and Counseling
Unity

~ Chapter 6 ~
Snatching Them From the Fire!
Sabrina D. Black

THINK ABOUT IT: **GET REVELATION**

"If sinners be dammed, at least let them leap to Hell over our bodies. If they will perish, let them perish with our arms about their knees. Let no one go there unwarned and unprayed for."
—Charles H. Spurgeon

"Brethren, if a man be overtaken in a fault, ye which are spiritual, restore such an one in the spirit of meekness; considering thyself, lest thou also be tempted. Bear ye one another's burdens, and so fulfill the law of Christ."
—Galatians 6:1-2 KJV

SECTION 1 - INTRODUCTION

1. What does it mean to be a WATCHMAN on the wall?

_____

_____

_____

_____

2. As a leader, how do you go about knowing those who labor
    among you? List at least five ways to get to know those with
    whom you co-labor.

_____

_____

_____

_____

3. What can you learn from each of the following Scriptures
    about leadership?
    A. Hebrews 13:17

_____

_____

_____

_____

    B. Ezekiel 13:17, 33:6

_____

_____

_____

    C. I Thessalonians 5:12-14

_____

_____

_____

_____

4. Read the following scenario and list each of the actions taken by the leader:

    Let me share with you a particular case. One of the hardest things that I have ever felt compelled to do was attempt to prevent a sister from traveling down a road that I knew from experience would lead to her demise and ultimate destruction. Believe me I did some serious soul-searching before I even approached her. I acknowledged my commitment to God and my responsibility to her as a leader. I thought about my own sins current and past. I thought about what I wanted and needed from my closest Christian friends. I thought about how hard it was for me to hear their admonishments and about my denial of my sin and my detachment from others because of it. Finally, I thought about God's love, grace, and mercy towards me. THEN I realized that I cared enough to confront my sister, so I went to her in love. I knew that it would not be easy. I even waited, hoping that another leader or even her family and other friends would address the issue and spare me the trauma and the drama. I knew she was not going to want to hear it and that it may jeopardize our relationship. Even still, "I am my brothers keeper," for God had laid her on my heart. My genuine love for her as one of God's children moved me beyond prayer to action.

    _____

    _____

    _____

    _____

    _____

    _____

    _____

    _____

5. As you think of the people you need to confront regarding sin in the camp, consider from the scenario Black provided above which steps have you taken? And which steps have you omitted?

   A. ACTION STEPS TAKEN

   _____

   _____

   _____

   _____

   B. ACTION STEPS OMITTED

   _____

   _____

   _____

   _____

6. In the quote at the beginning of this section, Dr. Spurgeon dramatically illustrates the intention of this chapter. Black further reminds us all (especially leaders) that our Christian duty as watchmen on the wall to the dying Sinner and wayward Christian is love and grace, not condemnation.

   A. Give an example of when you experienced love and grace from another leader.

   _____

   _____

   _____

   _____

   B. Give an example of when you gave love and grace to another leader.

   _____

   _____

   _____

   _____

7. According to Scripture in Isaiah 53:6a, AMP "All we like sheep have gone astray, we have turned every one to his own way." Given that we all at some point have been prone to wander, let us consider those things that have helped to deliver us from diverse temptations. List at least three things you do to overcome temptation when you are prone to wander.

   A. _____

   B. _____

   C. _____

8. What can you learn from the following Scriptures about God's commitment to you and others?

   A. Jeremiah 30:1-2

   _____
   _____
   _____
   _____

   B. Romans 5:8

   _____
   _____
   _____
   _____

   C. John 15:13

   _____
   _____
   _____
   _____

DO SOMETHING ABOUT IT: MAKE APPLICATION

SECTION II - WATCHMEN ON THE WALL

1. As leaders God has called us to be watchmen on the wall. According to Black, in Chapter 6, a watchman is like the _____ or the _____, he spies out the enemy and _____ a warning to the people so they can close all entranceways and keep the enemy out.

2. What are we watching for? Leaders are to watch and guard _____ for God! Leaders must watch for their own _____ as well, and ask God to search their _____ daily.

SECTION III
WHEN CHRISTIANS ARE PRONE TO WANDER

1. What does it mean to be "Prone to Wander?"

   _____

   _____

   _____

   _____

2. What are some great words of encouragement those who are prone to wander?

   _____

   _____

   _____

   _____

3. Instead of condemning those who are prone to wander, leaders should _____ and _____ those who have lost their way of the good news.

4. In the book by Black and Harlin, they knew that those who still were lost needed a vehicle through which they could honestly discuss their issues and seek _____ for

   _____.

5. Unfortunately when Christians are prone to wander (even if they have been restored and are in right standing with God) they are still _____. As a result of being prone to wander people are often _____.

6. As God's property, we are

   A. _____ by Grace

   B. _____ by Grace

   C. _____ by Grace.

7. According to Black, when Christians are prone to wander we need the _____ _____ of God's grace! Let me repeat that, we need GRACE, not condemnation.

   Even people who are walking godly and know how to walk occasionally stumble. The voice of the Lord is saying, "Whether you turn to the right or to the left, your ears will hear a voice behind you, saying, 'This is the way; walk in it.'" (Isaiah 30:21 NIV). We know and try our earnest best to avoid the 10 ways the Bible tells us not to walk (see Chart #1). We know that unless we adhere to the Word of God we are prone to wander. Yet we don't consistently do the things that we know to do like practicing the spiritual disciplines (see Chart #2) to help us walk in the spirit.

8. Look up the verses in Chart #1 and write what the Scripture
    says about how not to walk.

Chart #1

10 Ways Not to Walk

1. **As sinners** (Ephesians 4:17)

    _____

    _____

2. **As fools** (Ephesians 5:15)

    _____

    _____

3. **Contrary to God** (Leviticus 26:21-28)

    _____

    _____

4. **In darkness** (Psalm 82:5, Proverbs 2:13)

    _____

    _____

5. **In ways of the heart** (Ecclesiastes 11:9)

    _____

    _____

Chart #1 Cont'd

10 Ways Not to Walk

6. **After own devices** (Jeremiah 18:12)

   _____

   _____

7. **In lies** (Jeremiah 23:14)

   _____

   _____

8. **In pride** (Daniel 4:3 7)

   _____

   _____

9. **After the flesh** (Romans 8:1-4, 12-13)

   _____

   _____

10. **By sight** (II Corinthians 5:7)

    _____

    _____

Now that you have written what each verse has to say, pray regarding these areas. Pray for yourself as a leader, pray for those who serve as leaders to you, and those whom you lead. Spend time covering in prayer those leaders that are in your circle of influence. PRAY!

9. Review the Spiritual Disciplines in Chart #2. Make a list of the disciplines you practice on a consistent basis.

Chart #2

Spiritual Disciplines

- **Solitude** – spending time alone with God

- **Worship** – offering praise and adoration to God

- **Prayer** – talking to and listening to God regarding His will in your life

- **Study** – reading and meditating on Scripture

- **Confession** – admitting your transgressions to God and others

- **Submission** – responding to authority and seeking accountability

- **Fellowship** – mutual care and concern through time shared

_____

_____

_____

_____

_____

_____

10. Identify 2-3 areas of spiritual discipline that could use some improvement.

    A. _____

    B. _____

    C. _____

11. Identify at least one thing specifically that you plan to do to
improve in each of areas above.

    A. _____

    B. _____

    C. _____

Black discusses reading the Bible and identifying so much with
some of the characters as if they were her. She discusses laughing
at their foolishness, as well as some times crying over their sins.
She knows many of their stories very well because they were her
own. Consider the plight of the adulterous woman, the woman at
the well, King David, or any of the other men and women in
history with a tainted past or a scarlet letter.

12. Name 3 characters in the Bible with whom you identify and
give the reasons why?

    A. _____

    _____

    _____

    _____

    B. _____

    _____

    _____

    _____

    C. _____

    _____

    _____

    _____

SECTION IV - CONSIDER YOURSELF

As a leader you are in a position to see and discern issues in the lives of the people that God has given you watch over. We cannot turn the other way and pretend to not notice nor can we come off as though we have never sinned when we confront them. You who judge another do you not judge yourself? We all like sheep have gone astray.

I John 1:8-10 NIV reminds us, "If we claim to be without sin, we deceive ourselves and the truth is not in us. If we confess our sins, he is faithful and just and will forgive us our sins and purify us from all unrighteousness. If we claim we have not sinned, we make him out to be liar and his word has no place in our lives."

Yes, – "We all like sheep have gone astray. We have turned every one to his own way" (Isaiah 53:6 KJV). You may want to say, "No Lord, not me. I'm a leader." According to Black, it is when we come face to face with our own inadequacies, weaknesses, and sins that we are better equipped to minister to others. The words of Psalms 139:23 KJV, "Search me, O God and know my heart, try me and know my thoughts and see if there be any wicked way in me, and lead me in the way everlasting," are the scriptural basis for a Christian to regularly examine his or her heart for the purpose of confession of sins and repentance.

Because we tend to measure sin as big and small, we sometimes forget that many of our common responses are sinful and if not checked can lead us further astray. Dr. Don Dunlap of Family Christian Ministries provides an edited version of Charles G. Finney's checklist of 30 sins from "Breaking Up Fallow Ground." According to Finney, a renowned evangelist who was saved in 1821, it is a list of sins of which every person is guilty. Black has only listed twelve of the thirty areas. As you review this abbreviated version of the list, carefully consider, check and pray regarding the areas of your life where repentance and restitution may be necessary.

_____ 1. **Lack of Love for God** – Has someone else captured your heart, your thoughts or your time? God calls Himself a jealous God. Have you given your heart to someone or something else and offended Him?

_____ 2. **Neglect of Fellowship** – Have you made foolish excuses that have prevented you from attending fellowship gatherings with other Christians?

_____ 3. **Ritually Performing Duties** – Think of the times when you have spoken about God with a lack of faith or feeling. Recall the prayers that you have prayed carelessly, when you were in such a worldly frame of mind that you could hardly remember what you had prayed five minutes afterward.

_____ 4. **Lack of Love for Souls** – Look around at your friends, your acquaintances and your relatives and think of how little compassion you have felt for them. You have stood by, aware that they were lost and doomed for hell, and yet you failed to utter a single, fervent prayer for their salvation.

_____ 5. **Neglect of Family Duties** – Consider the kind of example you have set before your family. What direct, ongoing efforts do you make for their spiritual welfare?

_____ 6. **Failure to Watch Over the Brethren** – Christians are charged with the solemn duty to watch over one another in the Lord. How little do you know or care about the state of your brothers' and sisters' souls? What have you done to get to know them more personally? Do you see them falling into sin and yet you hold back and let them go on? Do you merely pretend to love them? Would you watch a close family member falling into disgrace and choose to remain silent?

_____ 7. **Envy** – Have you been jealous of people who were in a higher position than you were? Do you envy people who are more talented than you are? Does it cause you pain to hear certain people receive praise? Do you prefer to dwell on their faults rather than on their virtues? Do you rejoice in their failures rather than their successes?

_____ 8. **Bitterness** – Repent of all the times when you have harbored a grudge or a bitter spirit toward someone. Have you spoken of someone in an unloving way? Do you believe the best in people or do you suspect the worst?

_____ 9. **Hypocrisy** – Have you confessed sins that you did not really intend to turn away from? Have you prayed aloud in groups for people or situations, when your heart was cold and uncaring? Do you pray in front of others in order to be considered spiritual? Do you agree to pray for someone's need and then forget about it as soon as the person is out of sight?

_____ 10. **Failure to Control My Temper** – Are you an angry person? Do you often lose your temper with your spouse, your children, your friends, your neighbors or your work associates?

_____ 11. **Proud and Rebellious Heart** – Is it hard for you to admit when you are wrong? Do you long to be recognized by others and to receive credit for your accomplishments? Do you have a rebellious, disobedient, or unteachable spirit?

_____ 12. **Worrying and Being Anxious** – Do you trust God for your physical and spiritual needs? Do you often murmur and complain? Do you find fault with people easily? Do you have a critical attitude toward people or situations? Are you irritable, cranky, harsh or unkind?

According to Doug Britton, author of the Focus on the Family article, " Defeating Temptations: Biblical Secrets to Self-Control, "Whether our temptations are "minor" or life dominating, one thing is certain—we have them. You already know how hard it is to live a self-controlled life and how discouraging it is to fail again and again. You aren't alone. No one, other than Jesus, has lived a sinless life."

SECTION V - WHY WE DARE TO CARE

1. According to Black, what are some of the reasons that as
    leaders, we dare to care?

    _____

    _____

    _____

    _____

2. Whatever reason people give for leading sinful and
    uncommitted lives, other believers (especially leaders) should
    not give up on them. Leaders should continue to
    _____, to _____ them and if possible
    to _____ and _____ them.

3. According to Black, a leaders approach to wayward believers
    should be balanced. Over-exhortation by the use of too many
    Scriptures or as they may say,
    "_____" may drive them away.

4. According to Black, what will happen if a leader provides
    encouragement without dealing with the real issues?

    _____

    _____

    _____

    _____

5. When leaders confront about sin in someone's life, we need to
    be clear about what the Bible teaches on how to
    _____ as a Christian.

6. According to Black, the goal of confrontation is not to set people straight, but because as leaders we _____ and we know that _____ will accomplish that which it was sent forth to do.

7. In Psalm 86:15 KJV, we are reminded that "the Lord, art a God full of _____, and

   _____,

   _____, and plenteous in

   _____ and _____."

8. We are encouraged in Luke 6:36 to be like the Lord. What does the Word tell us to do?

   _____

   _____

   _____

   _____

9. God sees beyond our sin. He sees all that He has created us to be. When we look at the lives of those around us, whom we have watch over, we need to see them as God sees them. According to Black, we need to _____.
   We need to _____.
   These Christians have _____ and _____;
   leaders need to _____ in their
   _____. People need to feel that
   _____ is your goal.
   They need to feel God's _____ and
   _____ through you.

10. What is the difference between GRACE and MERCY?

   _____

   _____

   _____

   _____

11. As a leader, how would you go about telling or showing someone "The Christian Walk?" Give an example for each of the seven things to walk in that are listed in Chart #3.

Chart #3

The Christian Walk: 7 Things to Walk In

#	Walk in	Scripture Reference	Example
1	The Spirit	Galatians 5:16	
2	Love	Ephesians 5:2	
3	The Light	Ephesians 5:8-9 I Johns 1:7	
4	Watchfulness	Ephesians 6:18	
5	Christ	Colossians 2:6-7, II Corinthians 5:17-18	
6	Wisdom	Colossians 4:5	
7	Honesty	I Thessalonians 4:12	

12. In what way do you need to give others
room to allow Christ to empower?

_____

_____

_____

_____

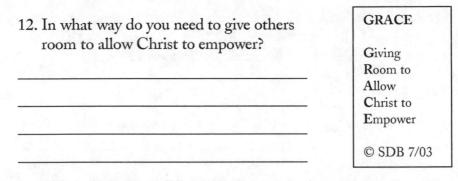

GRACE

Giving
Room to
Allow
Christ to
Empower

© SDB 7/03

13. If a person has been given truth, grace and love, yet refuses to
repent; then that person will answer to God, whether or not
you have said anything. But as the leader, you will have fulfilled
your obligation to God and those whom you are responsible
for. Consider the verse in Ezekiel 33:8-9. It shows the
accountability not only of those who sin but of those whom
God speaks to about those sins. What does the verse mean to
you as a leader?

_____

_____

_____

_____

SECTION VI
HOW TO SNATCH THEM FROM THE FIRE

1. Who is responsible for conviction regarding sin in someone's
life? _____.

2. It is our responsibility as leaders to give _____
and _____.

Even the most wayward person doesn't want to wander around in the dark and run the risk of being consumed by the fire. Think about the person you need to confront. As you snatch others from the fire, here are a few ideas, strategies, and pointers to consider:

- It's easy to be confrontational when you think that you are out of the line of fire. If you put yourself in the place of the person you are counseling or ministering, to you will show more compassion. We tend to give ourselves more grace than we give others.

- Before we approach a Christian who is ensnared in sin, we should try if possible to develop a relationship with him or her. People need to know they are loved and cared for. Establishing relationship gives a sense that you care. People don't care what you know, if they don't know how much you care.

- Remember encouraging someone takes time, and it may begin with finding out why wayward believers are disillusioned with Christianity. What is the reason they have gone astray? Those who want to help must probe gently and listen intently without harshly judging and labeling.

- When we encounter a fellow believer who is ensnared in sin but has little interest in escape because of disappointment or disillusionment, it is important that we encourage that person before he becomes hardened against God.

- People who are away from God often do not want to admit it or they simply cannot verbalize their problems. They know something is wrong, but they can't figure out what it is so they blame God and blame others. Help people see their responsibility in the choices they have made.

- The possibility also exists that some people have never truly understood the gospel and are not saved. If they are saved, it is also possible that the real reason for their disillusionment has not yet been uncovered. Perhaps they were not initially approached "in a spirit of gentleness" and love, and therefore they are still very disillusioned and perhaps even more so than before.

- Mature believers are to support new Christians and spiritually weak Christians by keeping them from getting into sin or falling further into sin through discipleship and accountability.

- Believers who because of their sinful past continue to struggle with certain sins may need more than occasional encouragement and exhortation; they may require constant supervision and support to keep them from sinning until new patterns of behavior are established.

- If encouragement and exhortation don't work, depending on the magnitude of the sin, church discipline may be necessary. This process will involve other leaders in the church and should be implemented with care.

- Always speak the truth in love in a spirit of love, gentleness, and meekness. People will quickly rebel when they think you are abusing your power.

- Don't sin against the people you have watch over by failing to pray. Seek God's guidance for how to approach them and the words to us. Pray, pray, pray; then pray about it some more.

- "Remember" was Paul's admonition, "as such were some of you." Let the redeemed of the Lord say so. We should tell others about how God's love and grace snatched each of us from the fire.

Begin to tell your story of being SNATCHED from the fire:

_____

_____

_____

_____

_____

_____

_____

_____

_____

_____

_____

_____

_____

_____

_____

_____

_____

_____

Now pray, and then proceed. May God give you favor as you watch for the souls of those in your care.

Remember every leader can benefit from *loving confrontation.*

PRAY ABOUT IT: MAKE INTERCESSION

Identify someone you need to snatch from the fire. Write a prayer for this person and fervently pray.

MEDITATE UPON IT:	CONTEMPLATION

Consider the people that you are in relationship with as a leader or follower. Then think about your responses to this chapter, *"Snatching Them from the Fire!"* Now fill in the chart below:

HELP	I need to receive from:	I need to give to:
Healing		
Encouraging		
Loving		
Perspective		

What is your action plan to receive what you need in each of the following areas?

Healing -
Encouraging -
Loving -
Perspective -

What is your action plan to give what is needed in each of the following areas?

Healing -
Encouraging -
Loving -
Perspective -

Every leader can benefit from:

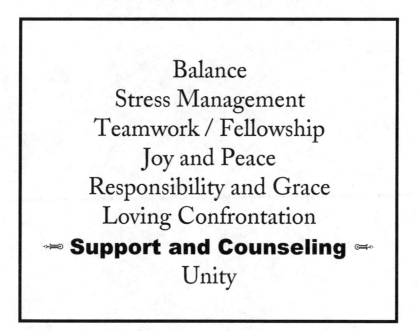

Balance
Stress Management
Teamwork / Fellowship
Joy and Peace
Responsibility and Grace
Loving Confrontation
Support and Counseling
Unity

~ Chapter 7 ~
When We Reach the Edge,
Where Do We Go For Support?
Brenda A. Jenkins

THINK ABOUT IT:	GET REVELATION

"Your success and happiness lie in you...Resolve to keep happy, and your joy and you shall form an invincible host against difficulties."
Helen Keller

"If the Lord delights in a man's way, he makes his steps firm; though he stumble, he will not fall, for the Lord upholds him with his hand"
(Psalm 37:23, 24).

The objectives of this chapter are:
(1) to help you recognize your need for help (completing assessments for all areas of your life)

(2) to give some suggested courses of action to become more

victorious in your life (place areas that need improvement on your Development plan).

Let's start by stating the problem as described by Jenkins, leaders off their path of being all God has called them to be. Let's look at some of the areas of your life to see if you are not on target. You should complete each of the assessments charts as it applies to you. We have attached an extra assessment chart that you can complete for areas not covered in this chapter. Your areas for improvement should then be put on your Development plan. (This is located at end of this chapter and on the CD that came with the workbook.)

DO SOMETHING ABOUT IT: MAKE APPLICATION

Let's get started. Today is the first day of the rest of your life. Change and self improvement are on-going. Next week you will be able to look back at this week and see progress. God Bless you and remember you can only be you, be the best you can be in all you do.

1. Jenkins states in the HELP! for Your Leadership book, chapter 7 that our primary relationship is our relationship with God. Using Matthew 6:33, her foundation is that all your needs in life will be taken care of if you live for God. Complete Assessment #1 – Kingdom Building

ASSESSMENT #1 - Kingdom Building

Matthew 6:33	Measurable Results		
	Daily	Weekly	Monthly
Worshipping God Spending time with God			
Bible Study			

Witness to others about the kingdom			
Praying			
Providing service			

Checks in shaded area are to be added to Development plan

2. Look up Ephesians 4:11-16, these are the gifts used in ministry. Complete Assessment chart #2.

ASSESSMENT #2

Ministry Spiritual Gifts: For the building up of the body of Christ (What is yours?)

Ephesians 4:11-16	Measurable Results		
	Identified	Developing	Operating In
Apostle function			
Prophet function			
Evangelist function			
Pastor function			
Teacher function			

Checks in shaded area are to be added to Development plan

3. Look up Romans 12:6-8, these are the seven motivational gifts. Complete Assessment chart #3. It is possible to have more then one.

ASSESSMENT #3

Motivational Gifts: Gifts to benefit one another (What is yours?)

Romans 12:6-8	Measurable Results		
	Identified	Developing	Operating In
Perceiver			
Server			

Teacher			
Exhorter			
Giver			
Administrator			
Compassion			

Checks in shaded area are to be added to Development plan

4. What is your marriage status? Complete the assessment chart # 4 based on your marriage status. There are blank boxes for you to add additional responsibilities.

ASSESSMENT #4

Only answer questions based on marriage status S = Single For Married use H = Husband, W = Wife	Actions reflect this statement	Actions does not reflect this statement
S - Must stay sexually pure – I Corinthians 6:9-10, 7:7-9		
S - Maintain a special relationship with God – 1 Corinthians 7:32 God's business is their business		
H - Loving leaders – Ephesians 5:25		
H - Love your wife, and be not bitter against them – Colossians 3:19		
H - Sexual pleasure – I Corinthians 7:1-5, Proverbs 5:18-19		
W - Must show respect, take care of home, and be helpmate – Proverbs 31, Ephesians 5:22-33, 1 Corinthians 11:3.		
W - Submit to own husband, as it is fit to the Lord – Colossians 3:18		

Checks in shaded area are to be added to Development plan

5. If you are a parent there may be many activities you get
   involved in with your children depending on their age. You can
   use this chart. Add activities that are missing to another
   assessment chart.

Parents Responsibilities (Proverbs 22:6)	Actions reflect this statement	Actions does not reflect this statement
Raise child to know and love God. (Deuteronomy 6:4 – 9)		
Provide love. (1 Corinthians 13)		
Provide instruction. (11 Timothy 3:14 – 17, Proverb 1:8, Proverb 6:20)		
Provide loving discipline. (Proverbs 29:17, Proverbs 19:18, Proverbs 29:15)		
Provide peace. Fathers do not provoke (Ephesians 6:4, Colossians 3:21)		
Provide safe, loving home.		
Provide healthy meals.		
Provide moral guidance.		
Provide protection.		
Provide opportunity for education (selection of school, meeting with teachers, be familiar with code of conduct and enforce) This could be separate activities if you need to work on any one.		
Provide health insurance.		
Monitor health and take to Doctor when necessary to maintain health.		

Checks in shaded area are to be added to Development plan

Let's discuss a couple of other areas. You may want to print off some assessment charts to evaluate areas you would like to work on.

6. It is vital that you eat healthy, are you eating a nutritional diet based on the four basic food groups?

_____

_____

_____

_____

7. What type of exercise are you doing?

_____

_____

_____

_____

8. Jenkins mentions healthy social relationships. List each social relationship you have. If none, add to development plan.

_____

_____

_____

_____

9. Are their some unhealthy social relationships you need to work on or let go? Please list.

_____

_____

_____

_____

10. From the book, we know that we are relational people. We need each other. What support groups do you have?

_____

_____

_____

_____

Complete the following assessment chart. If you do not have any or not enough, list ones you would like to develop on your development plan.

ASSESSMENT #5 – Available Support

Support	Yes	No
God		
Mentors		
Core Groups		
Professional Counseling		
Biblical Counseling		
Church		
Support Groups		

Choose the ones that are best suited for your situation

11. Are you a good steward of your money as described in the "HELP! for Your Leadership" book? If not, add preparation of budget and working the budget to your development plan. Complete Budget form on Workbook CD

12. How much sleep do you get every night? _____ hours
Do this test. Find a day when you can sleep as long as you want.
Write down the time you went to sleep. _____
Write down the time you woke up. _____
Does the total time you slept equal the number you put in question number 12? If you slept more hours than recorded above, add "getting _____ hours more sleep" to your development plan.

Development plan

Role/Job	Goal for accomplishing responsible activity with time frame	Estimate Completion date	Actual completion date	Progress (date with status)

Role/Job   **Assessment Chart**

Responsibility (List activities specific to the role use action/verb to state activity)	Measurable accomplishments for responsibility	Actions reflect this statement	Actions does not reflect this statement

Checks in shaded area are to be added to Development plan

Now pray, and then proceed. May God give you wisdom as you review your Development plan.

Remember every leader can benefit from *support and counseling.*

Steps for Improvement

1. Know what your call is and write your vision and mission statement.
2. Do an assessment in all the areas of your life. See assessment charts in this chapter and chapter 3.
3. Based on your assessment, write a development plan (form included at end of chapter).
4. Work your plan.
5. Do periodic check ups to make sure you are on track.
6. Repeat the process. This may be done more often when you have multiple issues. Take one day at a time, one issue at a time.

PRAY ABOUT IT: **MAKE INTERCESSION**

Read Psalm 37:23-24. Meditate on these scriptures and pray.

MEDITATE UPON IT:	CONTEMPLATION

Consider the people that you are in relationship with as a leader or follower. Then think about your responses to this chapter, *"When You Reach the Edge, Where Do You Go For Support."* Now fill in the chart below:

HELP	I need to receive from:	I need to give to:
Healing		
Encouraging		
Loving		
Perspective		

What is your action plan to receive what you need in each of the following areas?

Healing -
Encouraging -
Loving -
Perspective -

What is your action plan to give what is needed in each of the following areas?

Healing -
Encouraging -
Loving -
Perspective -

Every leader can benefit from:

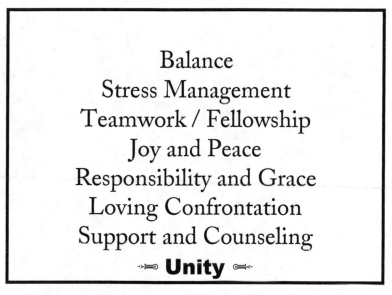

Balance
Stress Management
Teamwork / Fellowship
Joy and Peace
Responsibility and Grace
Loving Confrontation
Support and Counseling
Unity

~ Chapter 8 ~
When Unity is Impacted by You
Pamela J. Hudson

THINK ABOUT IT:	GET REVELATION

"The Bible is very clear regarding the attitude lay persons should have toward God's ministry gifts (those in position of leadership)."

1. I Chronicles 16:22 has a very clear warning. Discuss how this should be applied to our attitude toward leadership.

   _____

   _____

   _____

   _____

2. According to Ephesians 4:3, how can you be a "protector of unity?"

   _____

   _____

   _____

3. What has your experience been upholding or enforcing unity?

_____
_____
_____
_____

4. Discuss oneness as found in Psalm 133:1. Name ways to apply this principle.

_____
_____
_____
_____

5. Explain what you as a leader can do to successfully maintain the unity.

_____
_____
_____
_____

6. How have you contributed to disunity/disharmony?

_____
_____
_____
_____

DO SOMETHING ABOUT IT: MAKE APPLICATION

1. Anxiety as defined by the Holman Bible Dictionary is: a state of mind where one is concerned about something or someone. (Mark 4:19)

A. Describe the last time you exhibited signs of anxiety.

_____

_____

_____

_____

B. What was the outcome?

_____

_____

_____

_____

2. Frustration for leaders lies in their inability to know or understand their ministry role or call. Define your role or call in ministry.

_____

_____

_____

_____

3. How well do you understand your ministry gift?

   A. Very well

   B. Somewhat

   C. Not sure

4. Where is your spiritual dependence in your role as leader? Explain.

_____

_____

_____

5. How have you failed to comprehend your role as a leader in God's service?

    _____

    _____

    _____

    _____

6. What confusion have you seen among church leaders?

    _____

    _____

    _____

    _____

7. How has the lack of positive action by leadership or their negative attitude hampered church growth?

    _____

    _____

    _____

    _____

8. Discuss how politics, immaturity and fleshly emotions hindered spiritual growth of the congregation and personal growth of the leader?

    _____

    _____

    _____

    _____

9. Read John 21:16. Explain what our Commander-in-Chief ,Jesus Christ's, mandate for all in leadership.

_____

_____

_____

_____

10. How have you demonstrated the attributes of a doubting Gideon as a leader?

_____

_____

_____

_____

11. When was the last time you did something compulsive?

_____

_____

_____

_____

12. When have you been unable to make a decision? Discuss.

_____

_____

_____

_____

13. What do you as a leader worry about the most?

_____

_____

_____

_____

14. How important is personal integrity and character in leadership?

_____

_____

_____

_____

15. Write a short memo explaining your personal and spiritual lifestyle to your staff.

_____

_____

_____

_____

16. In chapter eight, Hudson shares a story by Dr. Freda Crews.

    1.   Do you have an account of a similar experience? _____

    2.   Do you know of an incident where the church leadership selected someone who hurt the congregation? _____

    3.   What were the affects?

_____

_____

_____

_____

17. What is God's Biblical response to worry? Quote a Scripture reference.

_____

_____

_____

_____

18. Share some examples (in the church or headlines) of leaders abusing their power.

_____

_____

_____

_____

19. We are having a leadership "crisis in confidence in this nation." Do you agree or disagree? Explain.

_____

_____

_____

_____

20. What can the Biblical Counselor offer that perpetuates change toward hurting leaders and congregations?

_____

_____

_____

_____

21. Nouthesis is a New Testament Greek noun meaning to admonish, warn, teach, and counsel. Define Nouthetic Counseling.

_____

_____

_____

_____

22. Who is the central figure in Nouthetic Counseling?

_____

_____

_____

23. Discuss how the following Scriptures promote unity and avert disunity?

   A. Colossians 3:16

   _____

   _____

   _____

   _____

   B. II Thessalonians 3:15

   _____

   _____

   _____

   _____

   C. Romans 15:14

   _____

   _____

   _____

   _____

24. What is the role of the Biblical Counselor in Nouthetic counseling?

   _____

   _____

   _____

   _____

25. How does Psalm 51:6 apply when confronting unBiblical behavior?

   _____

   _____

   _____

   _____

26. Discuss jealousy and its impact on leading and following.

_____

_____

_____

_____

27. How important is it for leaders to control their attitude and confession?

_____

_____

_____

_____

28. How did jealousy play a destructive role in the relationship of Moses, Miriam, and Aaron?

_____

_____

_____

_____

29. What leadership lessons can we learn from their actions?

_____

_____

_____

_____

30. Have you observed a "spirit of competition" among ministries?

A. What does this spirit do to the flow of ministry?

_____

_____

_____

_____

B. How does this speak to the insecurity of a leader?

_____

_____

_____

_____

31. Spend some time meditating on I Corinthians 13:4-8.

    A. Share some real examples of applications in your ministry?

    _____

    _____

    _____

    _____

    B. How can this concept bring healing and hope to the Body of Christ?

    _____

    _____

    _____

    _____

32. What could have been the fate of Elisha had he entertained a spirit of competition or jealousy toward Elijah?

    _____

    _____

    _____

    _____

33. Who are you jealous of in ministry?

_____

_____

_____

_____

34. Are you wrestling with a spirit of competition?

_____

_____

_____

_____

35. Have you used your position as leader for personal reasons only?

_____

_____

_____

_____

36. How have you wielded your influence for personal gain?

_____

_____

_____

_____

37. Would God be pleased with how you've used your leadership position? Explain.

_____

_____

_____

_____

38. When was the last time you successfully used your conflict resolution skills to bring about harmony or unity among ministers, staff, snd family?

_____
_____
_____
_____

39. Explain where hope for leadership comes from.

_____
_____
_____
_____

40. Looking at Jesus, what successful leadership traits or characteristics can you relate to as a leader in your ministry, home, or office?

_____
_____
_____
_____

41. Can you identify with Philippians 2:7? Explain. Give examples.

_____
_____
_____
_____

42. What is your mind set as a leader?

_____
_____
_____
_____

43. Are you a servant willing to serve or are you out to make a reputation for yourself?

_____

_____

_____

_____

44. How do you know you have a genuine love for people and ministry?

_____

_____

_____

_____

Remember every leader can benefit from *unity*.

PRAY ABOUT IT: **MAKE INTERCESSION**

1. Using the following Scriptures, write out an affirmation you can repeat daily.

   • Philippians 2:5, 2:3

   _____

   _____

   _____

   _____

- I John 5:5

  _____
  _____
  _____
  _____

- Hebrews 12:2

  _____
  _____
  _____
  _____

- Joshua 24:15

  _____
  _____
  _____
  _____

- I Peter 5:6

  _____
  _____
  _____
  _____

- Colossians 3:16

  _____
  _____
  _____
  _____

MEDITATE UPON IT:	CONTEMPLATION

Consider the people that you are in relationship with as a leader or follower. Then think about your responses to this chapter, *"When Unity is Impacted by You."* Now fill in the chart below:

HELP	I need to receive from:	I need to give to:
Healing		
Encouraging		
Loving		
Perspective		

What is your action plan to receive what you need in each of the following areas?

Healing -
Encouraging -
Loving -
Perspective -

What is your action plan to give what is needed in each of the following areas?

Healing -
Encouraging -
Loving -
Perspective -

Book 143

About Sabrina D. Black

Sabrina D. Black, M.A. L.L.P.C., C.A.C. – 1, is the Clinical Director of *Abundant Life Counseling Center*, an outpatient mental health facility, which emphasizes spiritual values. Among her credentials, Mrs. Black is a Limited Licensed Professional Counselor, Certified Addictions Counselor and Certified Biblical Counselor with 14 years of experience in individual, family, and group counseling. She has degrees in psychology and counseling. Sabrina has expertise in the fields of gambling addiction, sexual addiction and sexual abuse, relational problems due to substance abuse, issues relating to clergy and ministry leaders, marital conflicts and communication, boundaries, spiritual growth, stress, anxiety, burnout, and anger management.

As an author, national and international speaker for conferences, retreats, and workshops Sabrina's dynamic message of life's struggles, temptations, and triumphs challenges others to deal with the real issues of Christian living. She is much sought after consultant for schools, churches, corporations, and organizations.

Sabrina D. Black is adjunct faculty at Ashland Theological Seminary, Cornerstone University and a regional instructor for Christian Research and Development. Sabrina is president of the National Biblical Counselors Association, chairperson of the Black division of the American Association of Christian Counselors (BAACC), and an active member of several other organizations including MCA, ASGW, IAMFC, ACW-Detroit, AWSA and the Lydia Circle of Business and Professional Women.

Sabrina is an overseas Missionary and has been to Romania, the West Indies, and has made seven trips to Africa teaching, preaching, and reaching the masses with the gospel of Jesus Christ. Sabrina lives in Detroit, Michigan with her husband Warren Jose' Black. *Sabrina's goal is to help God's people live the Abundant Life through hope, help, and healing!*

For more information or to book Mrs. Black for speaking
engagements, or radio and television interviews contact:

Abundant Life Counseling Center
20700 Civic Center Drive, Suite 170, Southfield, MI 48076
Website: http://www.sabrinablack.com
Email: JadeBooks@aol.com
Phone: (313) 201-6286

About Christina Dixon

With over a decade of ministry to those seeking God as they rebuild their lives from the ravages of poverty, promiscuity, drug abuse, and homelessness, Christina is a woman for whom Christ has opened doors to serve Him through organizing food and reading programs, Bible teaching, seminar, workshop, and conference speaking, as well as music ministry.

A captivating, articulate, insightful, and often humorous speaker, she currently serves as President of Women's Ministry at New Hope Progressive Church on Detroit, Michigan's West Side.

In January 2005 she released a revision of her first book entitled, *How to Respect an Irresponsible Man*. Christina is also a contributing writer in the *Wisdom and Grace Devotional Bible for Young Women of Color*, by Nia Publishing and *HELP! for Your Leadership* by PriorityONE Publications. She is also listed among those who assisted in the selection the stories published in the recently released, *Chicken Soup for the African American Soul*.

She is an active member of the Writers Resources and Accountability for Publishing Group (WRAP), American Christian Writers-Detroit Chapter, (NBCA) National Biblical Counseling Association, the Lydia Circle of Business and Professional Women and United Christian Women's Ministries.

A wife, mother of five adult children, and grandmother of one, Christina and her husband, Elder Michael Dixon, live in Detroit, Michigan.

For more information or to book Mrs. Dixon for speaking engagements, or radio and television interviews contact:

PriorityONE Publications
Post Office Box 725, Farmington, MI 48332
Website: http://www.christinadixon.net
Email: info@christinadixon.net
Phone: 1-800-331-8841

About Pamela J. Hudson

Pamela J. Hudson, the teacher and speaker, teaches Biblical Counseling classes, and speaks to women and youth in workshops from Kalamazoo to Romania. Pam, the Certified Biblical Counselor has counseled singles, married couples, and youth since 1997 and is an adjunct instructor for Christian Research and Development. She is currently building her skills as a relationship coach to help people manage life challenges holistically. Pam, the leader and entrepreneur, has demonstrated her abilities in business, school, and church settings to facilitate, guide, and lead small and large groups. She is the President and CEO of Advanced Consulting and Marketing Services, where she assists small businesses and individuals planning to "Build a Better Tomorrow" by offering marketing, public relations, and media. As Director of the Board of Global Projects for Hope, Help and Healing, Pam works to promote this community based organization's vision for Detroit. Pam the freelance writer has been published through Nia Publishing, Grapevine Magazine, PriorityONE Publications, and in articles for BAACC, Co-Editor of the National Biblical Counselor Association Newsletter, and MAMFC a division of the Michigan Counseling Association. She is a member of American Christian Writers-Detroit and WRAP writing groups. Pamela resides in Detroit with her adult daughter and granddaughters.

For more information or to book Ms. Hudson for speaking engagements, or radio and television interviews contact:

Advanced Consulting & Marketing Services
19785 West 12 Mile Road, #242, Southfield, MI 48076
Website: http://www.AdvancewithPam.org
Email: wrapword02@yahoo.com
Phone: (313) 283-6089

About Brenda A. Jenkins

Brenda loves people. She states her purpose is to take her gifts and skills to help others. She is very transparent and has no problem sharing her victories overcoming rough times in her life. Brenda has the ability to see the expected outcome of any task and works to put plans in place to reach that end.

Brenda is well-versed in problem-solving, organizational and interpersonal skills. The Foundation for all that she does rests in her strong commitment to the Word of God. She is the mother to four adult children and the proud grandmother to twelve grandchildren.

At New Hope Missionary Baptist Church in Southfield, Michigan, Brenda served faithfully for seven years as the Ministry Director of the Biblical Counseling Ministry; a ministry birthed under her leadership. Currently, she is the Counseling Advisor and Outreach Facilitator for this ministry. As a Certified Biblical Counselor and adjunct instructor for Christian Research and Development, she teaches classes that will build up students and prepare them to confront themselves and counsel others with the Bible as the guidebook.

As CEO of ARIEL Connections her passion is "Providing Relationship Solutions to Organizations that Value People."

For more information or to book Ms. Jenkins for speaking engagements, or radio and television interviews contact:

ARIEL Connections
Post Office Box 22, Royal Oak, MI 48068-0022
Email: brenda.jenkins@ariel-connections.com
Website: www.ARIEL-Connections.com
Phone: (313) 719-1621

Leaders Self Care Workbook
HELP! for Your Leadership

Name _____

Address _____

City _____ State _____ Zip _____

Phone _____ Fax _____

Email _____

Quantity	
Price *(each)*	$10.99
Subtotal	
S & H *(each)*	$2.99
MI Tax 6%	
TOTAL	

METHOD OF PAYMENT:

❑ Check or Money Order (*Make payable to*: **PriorityONE Publications**)

❑ Visa   ❑ Master Card   ❑ American Express

Acct No. _____

Expiration Date (*mmyy*) _____

Signature _____

Mail your payment with this form to:
PriorityONE Publications
P. O. Box 725
Farmington, MI 48332
(800) 331-8841 – Toll Free
(313) 893-3359 – Southeast Michigan
URL: http://www.p1pubs.com
Email: info@p1pubs.com

HELP! for Your Leadership

Name _____

Address _____

City _____ State _____ Zip _____

Phone _____ Fax _____

Email _____

Quantity	
Price *(each)*	$14.99
Subtotal	
S & H *(each)*	$2.99
MI Tax 6%	
TOTAL	

METHOD OF PAYMENT:

❑ Check or Money Order (*Make payable to*: **PriorityONE Publications**)

❑ Visa   ❑ Master Card   ❑ American Express

Acct No. _____

Expiration Date (*mmyy*) _____

Signature _____

Mail your payment with this form to:
PriorityONE Publications
P. O. Box 725
Farmington, MI 48332
(800) 331-8841 – Toll Free
(313) 893-3359 – Southeast Michigan
URL: http://www.p1pubs.com
Email: info@p1pubs.com